Bob Bug and his mum are in the kitchen. Bob has a pen and a pad.

"Can you spell 'insects'?" says Bob.
"Yes," says Mum.

Bob sticks this on his den:
"Club for Insects".

Bob is sitting in his den. Ant taps on the den. "I am an insect," he says. "Can I come in?"

"Yes," says Bob. "You can be in the club."

Ant brings some toast. "Thank you," says Bob. Ant and Bob sit in the den and munch the toast.

Then Moth taps on the den.
"Can I come in?" she says.
"Have you got six legs?" says Bob.
"Yes, I have. I am an insect,"
says Moth.

Tap, tap, tap!

Moth brings some nuts. Bob and Ant and Moth sit in the den and crunch the nuts.

Then Toad taps on the den.
"Can I be in the club?" he says.

"Are you an insect, Toad?" says Bob.
"No, he's not!" says Ant.
"Toads like to EAT insects,"
says Moth.

"Then you can't come in,"
Bob tells Toad.

Cockroach taps on Bob's den.
He brings a drink and ten buns.
"Yum yum," says Bob. They eat
the buns and sip the drink.

Then Mum Bug yells, "Bob! Come in!"

Mum gives Bob some roast chicken.

"Eat up, Bob," she says.

"I'm not hungry," says Bob.